# GILES

**DAILY EXPRESS** AND **SUNDAY EXPRESS**

# CARTOONS

### FIFTY SIXTH SERIES

GILES CHARACTERS™ & © 2002 Express Newspapers

Published by

Pedigree®

The Old Rectory, Matford Lane, Exeter, Devon, EX2 4PS
email: books@pedigreegroup.co.uk
Under licence from Express Newspapers
ISBN 1-904329-01-2

GI 56

An Introduction by

**Sue MacGregor, OBE**

I was very flattered to be asked to write this foreword for the latest album of Giles cartoons. Although I was brought up far away from Great Britain, in South Africa, Giles cartoons so successfully made their way southwards - it must have been in albums rather like this - that they were part of my childhood there in the 1950's. British newspapers - and books - took some weeks to reach us then, on the old Union Castle mailships, which regularly plied their way between Southampton and Cape Town.

Each ship brought a bundle of booty which was on sale within days at the biggest local outlet, the Central News Agency. There was generally a rush for British papers and magazines, and at around Christmas time for the cartoon albums. It was thus that Giles and especially Giles' Granny became so familiar to me. I couldn't always follow the political jokes, but Giles' Granny was such an awesome and terrifying figure that I took to her immediately, even though - or perhaps because - she bore absolutely no resemblance to my own grandmother, a mild-mannered Scottish lady.

The best cartoons perfectly encapsulate the issues of the day. This is what Giles achieved so brilliantly, year after year. It's good to be able to look back at the best of them. Enjoy!


Sue MacGregor, OBE

"Dear me, how time flies – football here already."

"In case anything happens to me you'll find next week's sermon in my desk.
Don't forget to pay the organist. . . . Miss Peewit will help you with the parish mag."

"As that last smashing forehand drive lands in the far corner to bring him victory he leaps nimbly over the net to shake the hand of his opponent – Oh dear! His toe has just tipped the net . . . "

"Honest, Dad, there was tons of snow here yesterday."

"I dare you."

"Please can we have our ball?"

"Well, will your team be in the Final, dear?"

"Anybody here ride the last horse in the last race?"

Flaming June.

"From outer space – one unidentifiable object."

"Call from your sponsors, Al – want to know why their ad is appearing upside down on TV"

"Madam, my dogs insist that you are concealing at least one fox under there."

"Now there's a real fan – won't let a simple thing like the game being cancelled spoil his afternoon's sport."

"'Come on, boyso,' he said, 'let's see if we can make a Henry Cooper out of you'."

"Now be a good doggie and tell the gentleman if you've eaten his ball."

"The lady wishes to know if they've taxed wind yet. Have they taxed wind yet, Harry?"

"If the Labour Government ban hunting they can count on at least two votes – mine and the fox."

"We've been tobogganing – Dad's in Ward 10 but the sledge is all right."

"On the other hand I can't find a ruling that says if you merge two teams you can't play twenty two men"

"What kept you – the traffic hold-up on the M1?"

"And I tell you I distinctly remember putting my bike in here last year!"

"Oi don't see as how we can go much slower on our line unless we walk backuds."

"Then the driver stopped the train and said he suspected us of making derogatory remarks about engine drivers and made us all get out."

"And *I* say there *is* a pedestrian crossing here."

"Faster, Bert – he's gaining on you."

"Nice work, Mr. Coote, you've made it – just in time to knock off home."

"Another one blaming the Pope for making St. Christopher redundant."

"You're one of 'em who say we only need one-man trains – put your bike on yourself, mate."

Snow has fallen in many districts. More is on the way.

"What d'you bet this one says – 'Cold for the time of the year' or 'Dreadful weather for July'?"

"Well, here's your sun you've all been craving for."

"The merry month of Maying . . . With a fa, la, la, and a fa, la, la
. . . And in three weeks' time the nights start drawing in."

"Nothing's going to stop him giving the lawn its Easter hair cut with his new mower."

"I think people must be getting old if they can't enjoy the beauty of snow."

"Not bad, but not quite up to the standard of Torvill and Dean."

"Now the clocks have gone forward, Dad will have the nice light evenings to work in the garden."

"Bright idea of yours – taking them to the circus – wasn't it?"

"Dad, will you write a letter to the *Express*? Fred's just heard the first cuckoo - and GOT it!"

"We've had talks at top level and we've decided we're going to blast you off the face of the earth."

"Remember – we aren't playing polo, we aren't at the White City, we aren't Wells Fargo.
Just once to the pier and back nice and slow."

"Anybody seen one that matches this one? Escaped half an hour ago."

"Balance of Nature – Vera feeds 'em, we thin 'em out."

"Sorry to disturb you, Sir, but the Air Ministry inform us that thanks to your boy's kite all London Airport planes have been diverted to Gatwick and Manchester."

"They can feed me as many sex-educational films as they like – no one's going to convince
me that our relatives had anything to do with sex."

"Surely it's not too much to ask you to amuse them for a few minutes before you go to work – I've got them all day."

"We packed the children off to the Safari Park for a bit of peace."

"No, Father Bear WOULDN'T have found out quicker who'd been eating his porridge if he'd had the joint bugged!"

"Did you put a jumping cracker under Mr. Hettlethwaite's car?"

"Mother, did you remember to tell the boys to save their bath water for the garden?"

"We'd like separate bills and 5% off for cash."

"I suppose you can even remember what they had before Coronation Street, Grandma?"

"We sent the man next door a note saying we're holding his son hostage,
and he sent one back saying 'Thanks'"

"Dad, why do you always tell us if we don't do our homework we'll never get to the top?"

"Of course, boys and girls of intelligence learn infinitely more by rubbing shoulders with their playmates than they can possibly absorb in the classroom."

"I hope that's not my report he's writing – he's smiling."

"My dear Mrs. Peabody – If *I* had anything to do with it your boy would have left school when he was five."

"I suppose you'll always get one determined to rise above the common herd"

The strange desire of the British to paddle at least once a year. (Devon)

"Dad! Mum says come back and scratch out what you wrote in the Visitors' Book at once."

"Off they go – another load of little postcards saying we're having a wonderful
time and which won't arrive until long after we're home."

"Harry always takes an hour or so to make absolutely sure they're bathing in the nude before he reports them to the police."

"As a matter of fact we do not think this is better than taking one of those chancy holidays in the Med."

"I know I booked a two-week Round-Britain-Tour – but I didn't say anything about me going."

"It keeps them amused – they read about those boys who revived a whale with pails of cold water."

"Pity our flight was cancelled . . . Costa del Caballeria will never know what they missed."

"Of course it's not a very good snap of you, Grandma – that's a snap of the old harbour buoy
on the end of the pier."

"Stop arguing, Grandma, you know her rules – everybody out immediately after breakfast."

"This isn't Dad – it's a straw-packed dummy!"

"The girls think you should send these out as your Christmas cards."

"Now see here, Dr. Thomas, we know all about the B.M.A. survey on the shortage of accommodation for hospital doctors . . . "

"He says his case is urgent. He's been feeling a bit depressed since September 29 1905."

"I'd quit this underpaid job if I wasn't dedicated to scrubbing your sweet little neck every morning."

"It's no good you pesterin' me – Oi'm votin' for Gladstone, same as allus."

"The lady says can we find her paper as she thinks she voted for the wrong man."

"Frankly, young man, I do NOT recall patting your head in the last election and whispering I'd abolish schools if your father voted for me."

"From what I've seen of our elders, if I was old enough to vote I wouldn't vote for anyone who was old enough to vote."

"Grandma, you must let Vera vote for whom she chooses."

"Damn Joneses – he's wearing a WHITE tie!"

"Ladies! What would Her Majesty say – just because you say your neighbour's hung on to three of your chairs and she says you've nicked six of her forks."

"At least there's no danger of the ladies wearing the same hats today."

"I don't think she got the job, Dad."

"You should get a splendid view of Trooping the Colour from there,
madam – you're on the exact spot where Her Majesty will be taking the salute."

"My Grandma says hang everybody."

"How blessed is he who leads a country life, Unvexed with anxious cares, and void of strife!"–DRYDEN (1631-1700).

"Now say Sorry to Teddy for knocking him off the table – it's not his fault we've got another crisis."

"You might try and <u>look</u> pleased they've won a little pig."

"Inform Madam the marking on her valuable heirloom does not read 22 carat.
It reads 'A present from Blackpool made in Germany'."

"It'll be interesting to see what they do when they come to Tibby."

"You might have let him hit <u>one</u> as it's Father's Day."

"Daddy was very rude to Teddy. He says Teddy must stop phoning him at the office now the phone charges have gone up again."

"Mum, you know the new extension Dad's building himself to save massive builder's bills?"

"You'll have to read it to him later – he's dozed off again."

"Sorry Mum, I put all the clocks back instead of forward and Uncle Charlie and all of them have arrived for lunch."

"Know what I'm giving up for Lent? One or two things like Housework, Washing-up, Ironing . . . "

"If you wish to remain a permanent member of this family – no politics or religion!"

"It's your dad – he's invited them to hold their duel on our lawn."

"If he wins a million we might look forward to a new washer on this tap."

"Next – 'Make hole to take two inch waste-pipe'."

"You must make allowances for them getting bored with non-stop rain and Scrabble."

"Why do I think my husband is drunk in charge of a lawnmower? Because he's cutting the wrong lawn for a start!"

"You realise you are desecrating the image of one of the great freedom fighters who sought to free us from the Capitalist yoke."

"It's me husband, Sir – he won't come out. Says he's had about all he can stand of the outside world."

"Infidel!"

"Do stop mumbling, George. I asked you if anybody called during the week-end."

"Did you get one?"

"Which of these men attended that disgusting strip-tease concert?"

"Here we are, litter bugs."

"Here in the Gallery we have one of the finest art collections in the world."

"Do you know you're sitting on my Chihuahua?"

"This is James Bond, Secret Agent 007, licensed to kill with knife, gun, or bare hand – can I help you?"

"Thanks to you leaving me alone for five minutes, she leaped, and I am now committed to a life of married bliss."

"In you go, Fingers – If anything goes wrong me and the boys are behind you with the Jag."

"Oh dear, Rodney is expounding his theory that now we're the United States of Europe all the blighters should learn to speak English."

"I think Nessie's the biggest con in the wurrld. Aye, but she's good for the tourist trade."

"So you're from the Royal Commission investigating the law and legal services? That'll be £2,000 for a start."

"Let's spend Easter in that same little hotel we spent our honeymoon? Me too."

"I'll 'ave yer under the unfair trading act!"

"Mitzi, can we have just one teeny-weeny smile like we're topless in San Tropez?"

"Don't spoil it for him – flag made in Japan and shirt made in Hong Kong."

"Willie made up his mind he would only buy British-built cars – that was in 1932"

"Murdoch's uplifted your Times, Daddy – Mona Lisa on page three!"

"George sayeth: 'Time-and-a-half plus danger money', or thine fair daughter hath had it"

"Here comes one of 'em without a seatbelt – cover me, I'm going in"

"At least you haven't got a grandma who keeps telling you this heatwave
is nothing compared with the Punjab in 1908."

"There it is – June 6, 1944. You bet me £5 this was the war to end all wars. I bet you it wasn't. You owe me £5."

"If I'd known they were going to cut down council spending this much, I wouldn't have taken the bloomin' job."

" 'Ullo, 'Ullo, what we got here?"

"In the Spring a young man's fancy lightly turns to thoughts of love! You had any thoughts on the matter Romeo?"

"Where you went wrong is you should've turned right when you came out of West India Dock Road."

"Now for peace sake – don't tell the Missus we've had a drink."

"Knocked off for breaking and entering, if you must know."

"Never mind who hit who first – put the boy down."

"Hold it, Dad – Auntie Ivy hasn't quite gone yet."

"Of course Daddy will come and play table tennis with you, he bought it for you."

"On the Twelfth Day of Christmas my true love sent to me:
A bill for the tur-ur-key, another for the whi-is-ky, and one for the little fir tree."

"You'll have to find somewhere safer than the top of the cupboard to hide the presents – they've found Dad's."

"I don't know who it is – we thought it was you."

"You can get that damn thing off my desk for a start!"

"Right – on the show of hands Sebastian gets a reprieve – one of you go to the shop and get six large tins of corned beef."

"Elizabeth! You've been at the cooking sherry again."

"Grandma's been a great help. She's packed all the presents but forgot to label them which one's which."

"That's the holly and the mistletoe – now all we want is an almighty bang when dad blows the fuses, then we know it's Christmas."

"Lady, if it's mod you're after, Miss Selfridge is in Oxford Street."

"What do you say to me and you girls nipping down to the seaside for the afternoon?"

"No 'e aint – 'ee's a captin."

"Sergeant – I'm going to pretend I haven't seen something I *think* I've just seen."

"I said blast 'em and their manoeuvres – that's what I said."

Reynolds News

"Now you mention it – I *did* think those plans looked a bit odd."

"What's 'e think we are, ——————— ★ ! commandos?"

"Georgie! What a *lovely* beard!"

"The correct term, Private Wilson, when referring to a Commanding Officer is 'C.O.' Not 'there goes the toffee-nosed old basket.'"

"Of course, old man, you will appreciate that all I am telling you is most *frightfully* secret. . ."

"Oh Romeo, Romeo! wherefore art thou Romeo?"

"There is nothing, absolutely nothing, half so much worth doing as simply messing about in boats. . ."
*Extract from Kenneth Grahame's "Wind in the Willows."*

"I think Frampton is rather letting this Anglo-American nonsense run away with him."